ENDANGERED ANIMALS

ACTIVITY BOOK

Bear Grylls

 **Bear Grylls**

Our planet is full of magnificent creatures, and if you're very lucky you may be able to see many of them in their natural habitats while on your adventures. However, some of the world's most beautiful and important animals are in danger of dying out because human beings are hunting them or destroying their habitats. Travelling the world and seeing animals in the wild is incredible, but if we want to continue doing so then we have a responsibility to look after our planet and protect its wildlife, otherwise they may not be around for much longer.

In this activity book you will learn all about some amazing endangered animals, and find out what you can do to help protect them.

Bear

How to use this book

There are lots of amazing activities to tackle in this book, from mazes and word searches to dot to dots and counting games. Each activity has a symbol that tells you what kind of activity it is (see the symbol key below). Check the symbol first and then read the activity instructions carefully. You will find the stickers in the middle of the book and the answers on page 32.

Symbol key

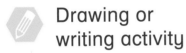 Drawing or writing activity

 Look closely activity

 Counting activity

 Sticker activity

WHAT'S THE DANGER?

Billions of animals share our beautiful planet. While many of them are able to find food, shelter, water, and mates, some of them struggle to survive. When an animal type, or species, is finding it too difficult to live, it is described as endangered. If nothing changes, the species will probably die out forever. This is called extinction.

Animals in every continent are endangered. Add the continent stickers to the world map and write the labels.

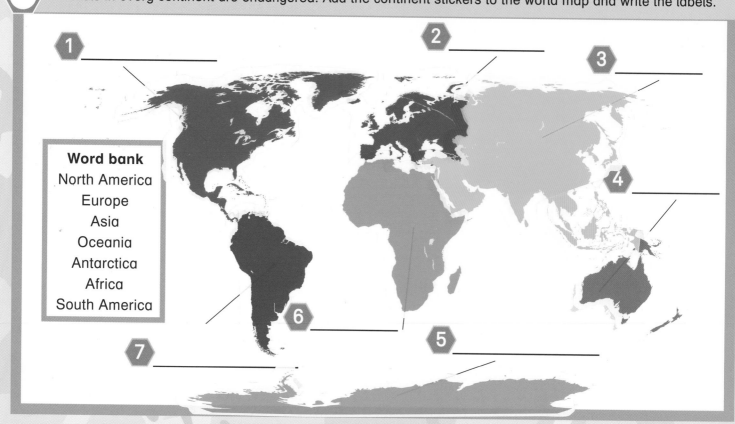

1 _____

2 _____

3 _____

4 _____

Word bank
North America
Europe
Asia
Oceania
Antarctica
Africa
South America

5 _____

6 _____

7 _____

Due to hunting, there are only about 60 Amur leopards left in the wild. Use the code to colour in this beautiful Amur leopard.

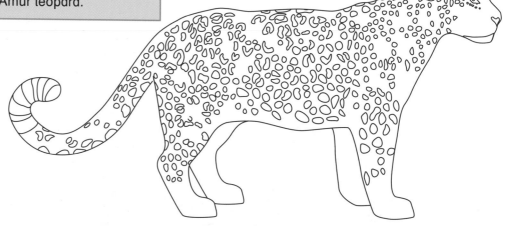

Colour code

Fur: sandy yellow

Spots: brown

Eyes: blue

The blue whale is the largest animal that has ever lived, but it is endangered. If this whale is the length of eight cars measuring four metres, how long is it?

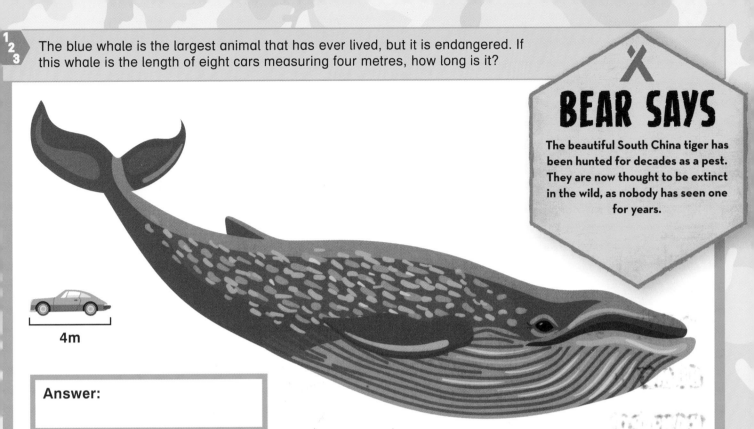

4m

Answer:

 Use the grid to copy this drawing of a dodo. These big birds lived on the island of Mauritius and they went extinct more than 300 years ago, after sailors hunted them for food and rats ate their eggs.

GIANT PANDAS

Giant pandas are large black and white bears that live in cool mountain forests of China. They eat bamboo, a tall woody grass that does not have much goodness in it – which means they have to spend half of their lives eating! The forests where giant pandas live have been cut down so people could farm and build homes for themselves.

 These endangered animals all live in cool forests, like the panda. How many can you find?

 KOALA

NUMBAT

KAKAPO

ECHIDNA

QUOLL

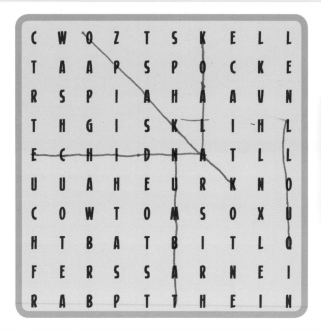

```
C W O Z T S K E L L
T A A P S P O C K E
R S P I A H A A V N
T H G I S K L I H L
E C H I D N A T L L
U U A H E U R K N O
C O W T O M S O X U
H T B A T B I T L Q
F E R S S A R N E I
R A B P T T H E I N
```

BEAR SAYS

The kakapo is the only flightless parrot in the world. They are in danger of extinction because humans introduced predators, such as cats and rats, to their habitats. There are less than 150 kakapos left in the wild.

 Red pandas live in cool mountain forests in Asia, often in the same places as giant pandas. They are the size of a pet cat, and eat bamboo as well as other plants.

Can you find the four differences between these two pictures?

Use the word bank to complete each sentence.

a) The place where an animal lives is called its

_____.

b) _____ is the favourite food of giant pandas.

c) The forests where animals live are sometimes

_____ to make way for humans. This is called deforestation.

d) The country of _____ is found on the continent of Asia.

Word bank

Habitat

China

Destroyed

Bamboo

Which one of these furry animals is not a bear? Find the stickers.

Sloth

Koala

Polar

Sun

Grizzly

Black

TIGERS

When a tiger stalks its prey it moves slowly, stealthily, silently. These are one of the most impressive members of the cat family, but they are in real danger of becoming extinct. Tigers are hunted by humans, and they have lost much of their habitat. They are beautiful animals with thick and patterned fur, which used to be treasured by people who wanted their skins to wear on their bodies, or decorate their homes.

 Tigers often hunt at night, when it is hard for their prey to see them. Can you match each of these rainforest animals to their name, using just their shadowy silhouette to recognize them? Find the stickers.

Buffalo **Deer** **Wild pig** **Monkey** **Fish**

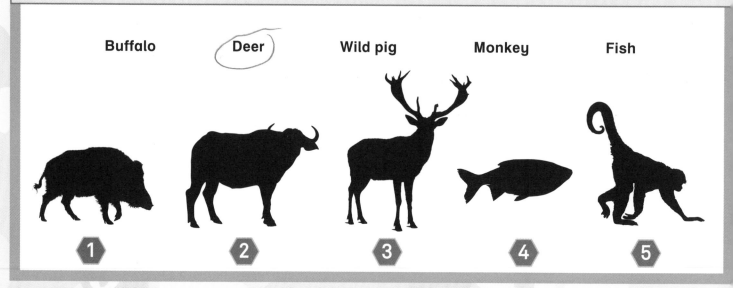

1   2   3   4   5

 Can you spot the four differences between these two clouded leopards?

These cats live in Asia and they are named after the cloud-shaped pattern of their spots.

BEAR SAYS

Though there are fewer than 400 Siberian tigers left in the wild, there is good news. In the 1930s there were only 40, but conservation efforts mean that the population is slowly rising.

Write a short poem about a tiger. The words in the word bank may be useful.

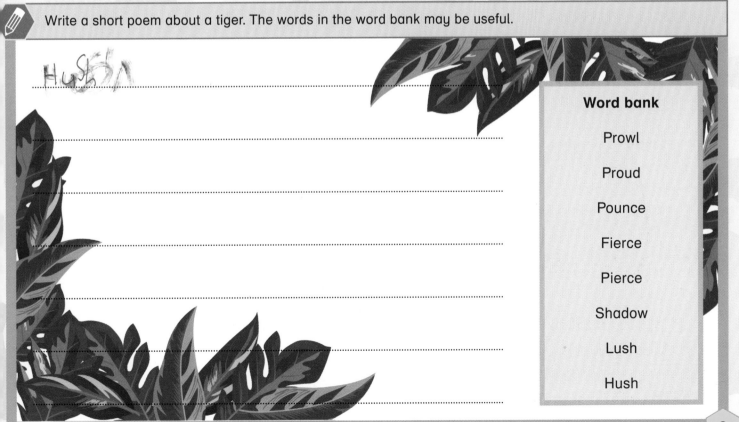

Hush

Word bank

Prowl

Proud

Pounce

Fierce

Pierce

Shadow

Lush

Hush

RHINOCEROSES

A rhinoceros is a huge, horned, grass-eating animal that spends the hottest part of the day slumbering in the cool shade, or wallowing in mud. Rhinos have one or two horns, and they have been hunted to near-extinction for these horns. Some people wrongly believe that the horns can be used to cure illness.

There are five species of rhinoceros: Sumatran, Javan, Indian, White, and Black.

Follow the line from each rhino and write in its name. Find the stickers.

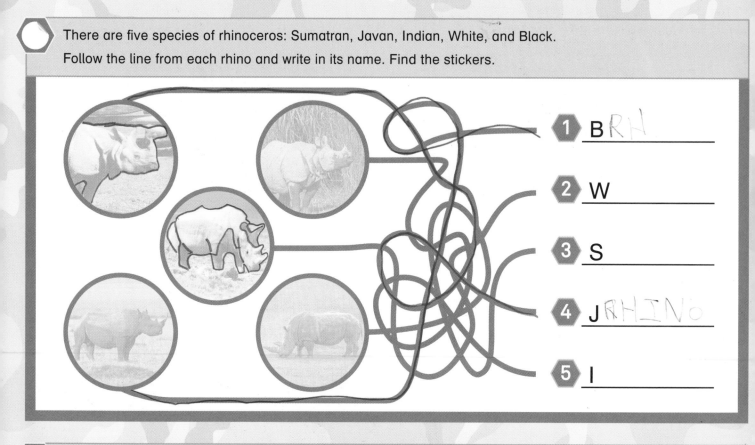

1 B RH _____

2 W _____

3 S _____

4 J RHINO _____

5 I _____

How many words can you make from the word "rhinoceros"?

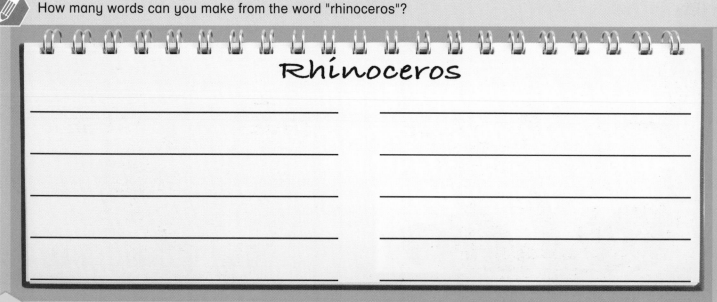

Rhinoceros

QUICK QUIZ

What have you learned in this section? Test your knowledge! Read the questions below and circle the correct answer.

1 There are only 60 dodos left in the world.

TRUE   **FALSE**

2 Pandas live in Africa.

TRUE   **FALSE**

3 A tiger's stripes work as camouflage.

TRUE   **FALSE**

4 Tigers are hunted for their skins.

TRUE   **FALSE**

5 Some people believe that rhinoceros horns are good for your skin.

TRUE   **FALSE**

GORILLAS

For many years, people thought that gorillas were dangerous animals. They may be big and strong, but gorillas are gentle, plant-eating giants that only attack humans to protect their families. Gorillas live in Africa, but they are in danger of becoming extinct because they have been hunted by people, and their forest homes have been destroyed.

Find the stickers for these unusual-looking monkeys.

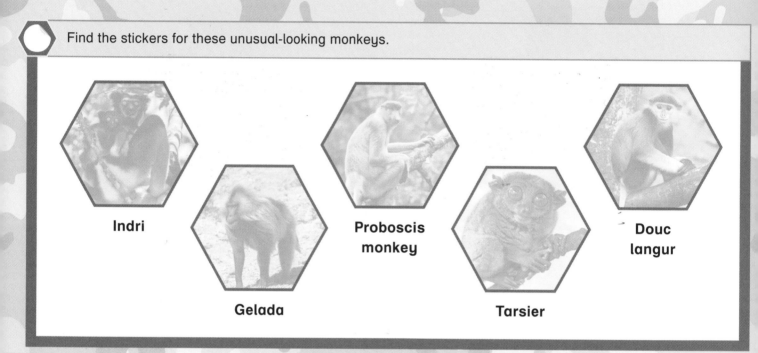

Indri

Gelada

Proboscis monkey

Tarsier

Douc langur

 Gorillas belong to a group of animals called primates. It includes apes and monkeys. How many of these endangered primates can you find?

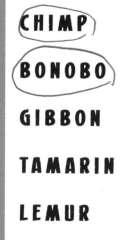

CHIMP

BONOBO

GIBBON

TAMARIN

LEMUR

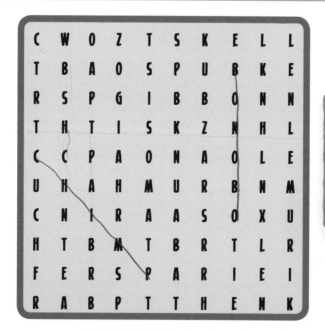

C	W	O	Z	T	S	K	E	L	L
T	B	A	O	S	P	U	B	K	E
R	S	P	G	I	B	B	O	N	N
T	H	T	I	S	K	Z	N	H	L
C	C	P	A	O	N	A	O	L	E
U	H	A	H	M	U	R	B	N	M
C	N	I	R	A	A	S	O	X	U
H	T	B	M	T	B	R	T	L	R
F	E	R	S	P	A	R	I	E	I
R	A	B	P	T	T	H	E	N	K

BEAR SAYS

The gorilla population was on the rise until war in Rwanda put a stop to many of the efforts to save the species. Now there are fewer than 600 mountain gorillas left.

A family of gorillas is protected by the strongest father in the group, called a silverback. They are named after their black fur, which is speckled with grey. Join the dots to reveal a big, beautiful silverback.

How much do you know about monkeys and apes? Answer these questions to find out.

A. Apes don't have tails, but monkeys do.

TRUE

FALSE

B. Humans belong to the primate family too.

TRUE

FALSE

C. Primate babies are called cubs.

TRUE

FALSE

TURTLES

For more than 100 million years, turtles have swum across the oceans to reach beaches where they lay their eggs. In just 200 years, humans have brought many of them close to extinction. Turtles belong to a group of animals called reptiles. They have a tough, bony shell that protects them from ocean predators such as sharks and giant octopuses.

 A mother loggerhead turtle has to come onto land to lay her eggs, and then she returns to the sea. The babies must find their way back to the sea by themselves, but they can be confused by bright lights, or eaten by dogs and sea birds. Help the baby turtle through the maze to reach the sea safely.

 Leatherback turtles swim across the oceans to reach their breeding grounds. They can cover 6,000 km in a year.

a) If a leatherback turtle swam 10 km every day, how many many kilometres would it swim in the month of June?

b) Would it swim further in February?

Unscramble the names of these three marine turtles.

Find the stickers to complete these pictures of other endangered (or extinct) reptiles.

1 HEDAGERLOG

2 HEATBRACKLE

3 SHILLBAWK

1 Loggerhead

2 Leatherback

3 Hawksbill

Galapagos Tortoise

Cuban crocodile

Dumeril's boa

King cobra

BEAR SAYS

The giant Galapagos tortoise can only be found on the Pacific island of Galapagos. Although they can live up to 100 years, they are in danger of dying out because they are hunted for their meat.

AFRICAN WILD DOGS

African wild dogs live in large family groups and share the work of hunting and looking after pups. These clever animals were once common in Africa, but they are now battling for survival. African wild dogs live in the savannah (grasslands) of Africa where they hunt large animals, including zebras and wildebeest.

Can you spot four differences between these two pictures of African wild dogs?
They are sometimes called painted dogs.

Which two of these animals don't belong in the African savannah?

What have you learned in this section? Test your knowledge! Read the questions below and circle the correct answer.

1 Gorillas are very dangerous animals.

2 The head of a gorilla family is called a silverback.

TRUE   FALSE

TRUE   FALSE

3 Turtles lay their eggs on land.

TRUE   FALSE

4 Turtles can live for up to 100 years.

5 African wild dogs are herbivores.

TRUE   FALSE

TRUE   FALSE

POLAR BEARS

The chilly Arctic is the area around the North Pole. It is named after the Arctic Sea, which gets so cold that parts of it freeze into solid ice. This ice is home to some incredible animals, which manage to survive in one of the world's harshest habitats. Polar bears live in the Arctic, but their future is threatened by climate change. The world is getting warmer and this makes the ice melt, so there are fewer places for polar bears to live.

Scientists attach special collars to bears, so they can use satellites to follow them as they travel in the Arctic.

If a team of scientists can collar two bears a day, how many bears can they collar in two weeks?

2 x 7 x 2 = _28_

BEAR SAYS

Many Arctic animals are in danger because of climate change. As the planet heats up, the ice around the North Pole melts and the habitat of many animals gradualy disappears.

Are these statements true or false?

a. Polar bears live in the Antarctic.

TRUE

FALSE

b. There is more Arctic ice in the winter than in the summer.

TRUE

FALSE

c. The world is getting cooler.

TRUE

FALSE

✏️ Write down three things you can do to help stop the damage done to the planet by climate change.

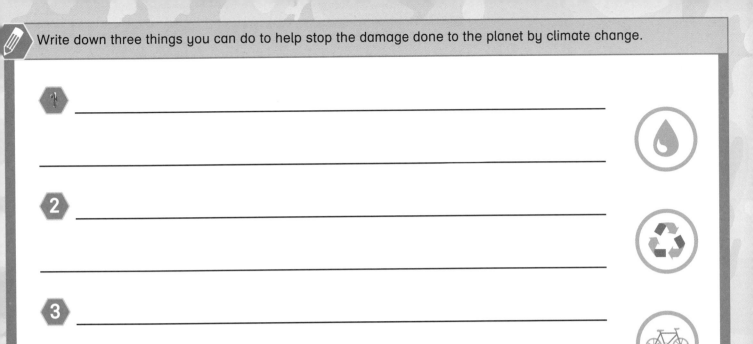

1 _____

_____

2 _____

_____

3 _____

_____

Which two of these animals are out of place in the Arctic wilderness? Find the stickers.

19

PARROTS

Parrots are brightly coloured birds that mostly live in warm places, often in rainforests. They are noisy, intelligent birds that eat fruit, berries, nuts, seeds, bugs, and flowers. Many of these beautiful birds have been captured and sold as pets, but they are also endangered because their rainforest homes are being destroyed.

Follow the lines to reveal the name of each of these endangered parrots. Add the stickers.

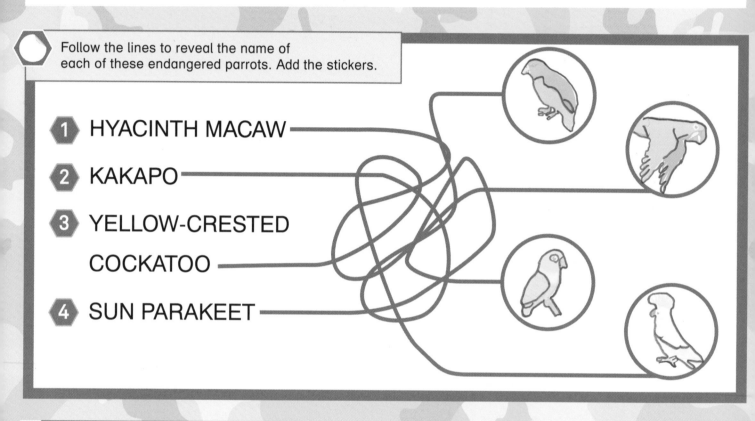

1. HYACINTH MACAW

2. KAKAPO

3. YELLOW-CRESTED
   COCKATOO

4. SUN PARAKEET

Circle all the foods that a parrot might eat.

Complete the pictures of these rainforest birds with the right stickers.

Southern crowned pigeon

Philippine eagle

Hyacinth macaw

Yellow-crested cockatoo

Sun parakeet

BEAR SAYS

The Spix's macaw is thought to be extinct in the wild, as people capture them to keep as pets. There may be around 90 left in captivity, but unless they are allowed to breed they will die out.

Forests are often cut down and destroyed so people can build roads and homes or create new farmland. This is called deforestation.

How many words can you make from the letters in 'deforestation'?

Deforestation

ELEPHANTS

Elephants are the largest animals that live on land. They are also some of the smartest! An elephant family is led by a female. She remembers the best places to find food and water, so she is in charge of taking her family on long journeys, called migrations. Elephants have long teeth, or tusks, which are made of a hard white material called ivory. Poachers kill elephants for their tusks, which are then made into ornaments and jewellery.

 There are two main types of elephant: Asian elephants and African elephants. There are some differences between elephants that live in Africa and Asia. How many of them do you know?

Tick the true statements.

1. African elephants are bigger than Asian elephants.

2. Asian elephants have bigger ears.

3. African elephants are listed as 'Vulnerable', but Asian elephants are 'Endangered'.

4. Asian elephants hunt other animals to eat.

5. An Asian elephant's trunk has one finger-like tip, but an African elephant's trunk has two.

African savannah elephant

Asian elephant

 Use the grid to copy this picture of an Asian elephant.

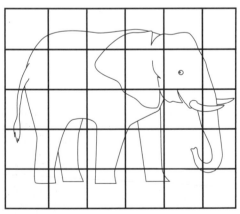

Elephants in Mali have to go on long migrations to find water. Help this baby elephant find its way to the rest of the herd, who are already at the watering hole.

Elephants may be the biggest animals on land, but giraffes are the tallest! They live alongside African elephants, using their long necks to reach the juiciest leaves.

Can you spot four differences between these two pictures?

SHARKS

Many people are scared of sharks, but they have much more to fear from us. These predators hunt fish and other ocean-living creatures. Sharks are superb swimmers, and use an excellent sense of smell to find their prey. Some sharks are hunted for food, or die after getting caught in fishing nets.

1 2 3 Sharks have several rows of teeth, so as old teeth fall out, new ones can move in to replace them.

Count how many teeth you can see in this shark's mouth.

Write the number here: _____

What shape are they?

a) round

b) square

c) triangular

Count how many teeth you have and write the number here: _____

How many of these types of shark can you find?

BLUE

GOBLIN

HAMMERHEAD

NURSE

WOBBEGONG

DOGFISH

C	W	O	D	O	G	F	I	S	H
T	B	A	P	G	P	U	B	K	E
R	S	L	N	I	O	B	O	N	N
T	H	T	U	S	K	B	N	H	L
C	C	P	R	E	N	A	L	L	E
U	H	A	S	M	U	R	B	I	M
C	N	I	E	A	A	S	O	X	N
H	A	M	M	E	R	H	E	A	D
H	E	R	S	P	A	R	I	E	I
R	G	N	O	G	E	B	B	O	W

BEAR SAYS

There are only an estimated 3,500 great white sharks left in the wild. Humans have been overfishing in their habitat, destroying the sharks' food supply.

QUICK QUIZ

 What have you learned in this section? Test your knowledge! Read the questions below and circle the correct answer.

1 Polar bears are threatened because their habitat is disappearing.

TRUE FALSE

2 People like to catch exotic birds to keep as pets.

TRUE FALSE

3 Elephants aren't very clever.

TRUE FALSE

4 Elephants are the biggest land mammals in the world.

TRUE FALSE

5 There are only 20 great white sharks left in the wild.

TRUE FALSE

ORANG-UTANS

The Asian islands of Borneo and Sumatra are home to apes called orang-utans. They spend most of their lives in the rainforest canopy, where they find fruit to eat. Young orang-utans stay with their mothers until they are about eight years old, and she teaches them how to build nests to sleep in, and where to find the best fruits.

 Baby orang-utans are jungle acrobats, and they love to climb and hang upside-down! Can you colour in this baby orang-utan as it plays?

BEAR SAYS

The orang-utan population has declined by around 50 percent over the past 60 years. They used to roam across South Asia, but are now only found on two islands – Borneo and Sumatra.

Stinky green durian fruits are one of an orang-utan's favourite foods, along with pink prickly rambutans and red, green, and orange mangoes.

Write the correct name next to these fruits.

1 _appaS_

2 _eggs_

3 _pinapall_

The orang-utans' home is being cut down to make way for palm trees. Farmers grow palm trees because they can be used to make palm oil.

These things are all made using palm oil. How many can you find?

LIPSTICK

SHAMPOO

CHOCOLATE

BISCUITS

CAKE

SOAP

MARGARINE

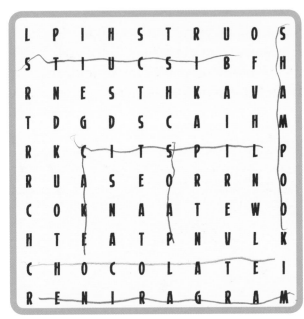

L	P	I	H	S	T	R	U	O	S
S	T	I	U	C	S	I	B	F	H
R	N	E	S	T	H	K	A	V	A
T	D	G	D	S	C	A	I	H	M
R	K	C	I	T	S	P	I	L	P
R	U	A	S	E	O	R	R	N	O
C	O	K	N	A	A	T	E	W	O
H	T	E	A	T	P	N	V	L	K
C	H	O	C	O	L	A	T	E	I
R	E	N	I	R	A	G	R	A	M

 Orang-utans have to spend a lot of time travelling through the forest looking for food, but the sun sets at 6pm. Look at the clock and work out how many hours of daylight are left before the orang-utan must go to sleep.

Write your answer here:

_____

27

WHALES

Whales and dolphins belong to the same group of incredible animals, called cetaceans. They are very clever and, although they spend their whole lives in the sea, they breathe air like animals that live on land. The largest whales are called the great whales. Out of 13 species of great whale, seven of them are endangered or vulnerable because humans have hunted them in the past. Today some countries still choose to hunt whales.

Dolphins and porpoises belong to the whale family. Most dolphins have a pointed snout, called a "beak", while porpoises have a rounded snout. Spot the porpoise, and add stickers into the spaces.

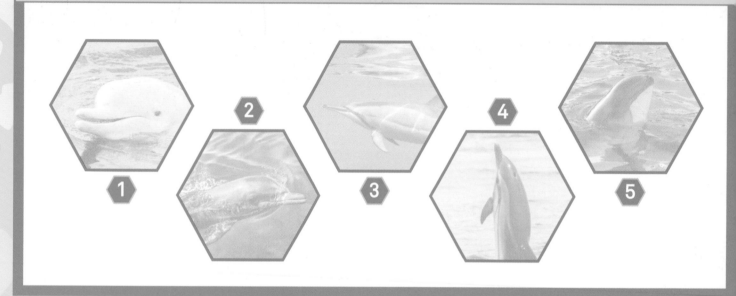

Use a sticker to complete this picture of a narwhal. This Arctic animal is at risk of becoming endangered because climate change and pollution are damaging its habitat.

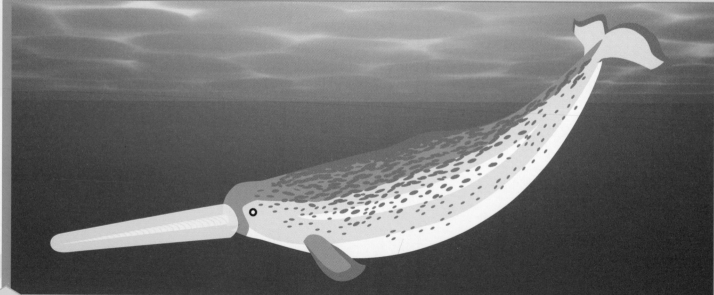

Help the baby whale find its mum. Baby whales and dolphins have to stay close to their mums all the time, so hurry!

Complete the dot to dot to reveal a picture of a baiji. A baiji a dolphin that once lived in the Yangtze River of China, but no one has seen a baiji for a long time. They are probably extinct.

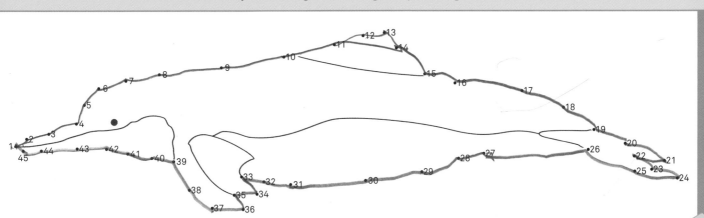

STRANGE AND IN DANGER

Have you ever heard of these endangered animals? Not all endangered animals are cute, furry, or famous – but they still need human help to survive.

 Put the correct stickers next to the descriptions of these animals.

 **Malayan tapir:** This pig-like animal has long legs and a long snout. It lives in Southeast Asia.

 **Scimitar-horned oryx:** An oryx is a member of the cattle, or cow, family. This oryx species is now extinct in the wild, although some survive in captivity.

 **Panamanian golden frog:** This little rainforest frog has been wiped out by a fast-spreading disease. It's probably extinct in the wild.

 **North Brother Island Tuatara:** This lizard-like animal only lives on one small island, near New Zealand. It grows very slowly, but can reach 100 years of age!

 Scientists work very hard to conserve, or save, habitats and the animals and plants that live in them. The work they do is called conservation.

How many words can you make from the word "conservation"?

Conservation

QUICK QUIZ

What have you learned in this section? Test your knowledge! Read the questions below and circle the correct answer.

 1 Orang-utans live on the islands of Borneo and Sumatra.

TRUE   FALSE

 2 Orang-utans eat mostly insects.

TRUE   FALSE

3 Some countries still hunt whales today.

TRUE   FALSE

4 There are only 1,000 baijis left.

TRUE   FALSE

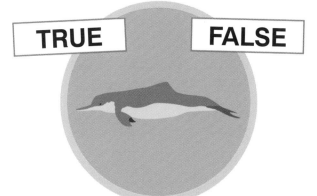

5 The Panamanian golden frog may have been wiped out in the wild by disease.

TRUE   FALSE

ANSWERS

Page 4
Continents
1. North America; 2. Europe;
3. Asia; 4. Oceania;
5. Antarctica; 6. Africa;
7. South America

Page 5
Blue whale
The whale is 32 m long.

Page 6
Word search

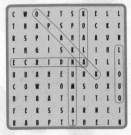

Spot the difference

Page 7
Fill in the gaps
a) Habitat b) Bamboo
c) Destroyed d) China

Odd one out
Sloth is not a bear.

Page 8
Shadows
1. Wild pig; 2. Buffalo; 3. Deer;
4. Fish; 5. Monkey

Spot the difference

Page 10
1. Black; 2. White; 3. Sumatran;
4. Javan; 5. Indian

Page 11
1. False; 2. False; 3. True;
4. True; 5. False

Page 12
Word search

Page 13
Dot to dot

True or false
A & B are true.
C is false; primate babies
are called babies!

Page 14
Maze

Maths
a) 30 x 10 = 300 km
b) No, because June has
30 days but February has
28 days.

Page 15
Unscramble
1. Loggerhead; 2. Leatherback;
3. Hawksbill

Page 16
Spot the difference

Odd one out

Page 17
1. False; 2. True; 3. True;
4. True; 5. False

Page 18
Maths
28 polar bears
True or False
a. False; b. True;
c. False

Page 20
Parrot foods
Parrots can eat fruits, nuts,
berries, flowers, and seeds.

Page 22
Elephant quiz
1, 3, 5 are true.

Page 23
Maze

Spot the difference

Page 24
Shark teeth
The shark has approx 40 teeth.
They are triangular.

Word search

Page 25
1. True; 2. True; 3. False;
4. True; 5. False

Page 26
Find the fruit
1. Mango
2. Rambutans
3. Durian fruit

Page 27
Word search

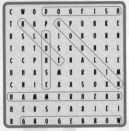

Orangutan sunset
5 hours

Page 28
Find the porpoise
5 is the porpoise

Page 29
Maze

Dot to dot

Page 31
1. True; 2. False; 3. True;
4. False; 5. True